THE ROYAL HORTICULTURAL SOCIETY
DIARY 2004

Commentary by Brent Elliott

Illustrations from the
Royal Horticultural Society's Lindley Library

FRANCES LINCOLN

Frances Lincoln Limited
4 Torriano Mews
Torriano Avenue
London NW5 2RZ
www.franceslincoln.com

The Royal Horticultural Society Diary 2004
Copyright © Frances Lincoln Limited 2003

British Library cataloguing-in-publication data
A catalogue record for this book is available from the British Library

ISBN 0-7112-2088-3

Printed in China
First Frances Lincoln edition 2003

RHS FLOWER SHOWS 2004

All shows feature a wide range of floral exhibits staged by the nursery trade, with associated competitions
reflecting seasonal changes and horticultural sundries. With the exception of the shows held at Torquay,
Malvern, Chelsea, Wisley, Hampton Court, and Tatton Park, all RHS Flower Shows will be held in one or both
of the Society's Horticultural Halls in Greycoat Street and Vincent Square, Westminster, London SW1.

**The dates given are correct at the time of going to press, but before travelling to a Show,
we strongly advise you to check with the Diary Dates section of the RHS Journal *The Garden*,
or telephone the 24-hour Flower Show Information Line (020 7649 1885) for the latest details.**

FRONT COVER
A drawing of *Paeonia officinalis*, dated 1784, by M. Smith. Reginald Cory bequest, 1936.

BACK COVER
A drawing of honeysuckle (*Lonicera periclymenum*) and spotted figwort (*Scrophularia nodosa*) by Winifred Bussey.
Geraldine Bussey bequest, 2001.

TITLE PAGE
A drawing of the strawberry tree (*Arbutus unedo*), probably 1780s, by Margaret Meen. Reginald Cory bequest, 1936.

OVERLEAF, LEFT
A coloured stipple engraving after Pierre Antoine Poiteau of a lemon cultivar, 'Limone di ferrari',
from *Histoire Naturelle des Orangers* (1818–22), by Antoine Risso and Poiteau. Reginald Cory bequest, 1936.

CALENDAR 2004

JANUARY
M	T	W	T	F	S	S
			1	2	3	4
5	6	7	8	9	10	11
12	13	14	15	16	17	18
19	20	21	22	23	24	25
26	27	28	29	30	31	

FEBRUARY
M	T	W	T	F	S	S
						1
2	3	4	5	6	7	8
9	10	11	12	13	14	15
16	17	18	19	20	21	22
23	24	25	26	27	28	29

MARCH
M	T	W	T	F	S	S
1	2	3	4	5	6	7
8	9	10	11	12	13	14
15	16	17	18	19	20	21
22	23	24	25	26	27	28
29	30	31				

APRIL
M	T	W	T	F	S	S
			1	2	3	4
5	6	7	8	9	10	11
12	13	14	15	16	17	18
19	20	21	22	23	24	25
26	27	28	29	30		

MAY
M	T	W	T	F	S	S
					1	2
3	4	5	6	7	8	9
10	11	12	13	14	15	16
17	18	19	20	21	22	23
24	25	26	27	28	29	30
31						

JUNE
M	T	W	T	F	S	S
	1	2	3	4	5	6
7	8	9	10	11	12	13
14	15	16	17	18	19	20
21	22	23	24	25	26	27
28	29	30				

JULY
M	T	W	T	F	S	S
			1	2	3	4
5	6	7	8	9	10	11
12	13	14	15	16	17	18
19	20	21	22	23	24	25
26	27	28	29	30	31	

AUGUST
M	T	W	T	F	S	S
						1
2	3	4	5	6	7	8
9	10	11	12	13	14	15
16	17	18	19	20	21	22
23	24	25	26	27	28	29
30	31					

SEPTEMBER
M	T	W	T	F	S	S
		1	2	3	4	5
6	7	8	9	10	11	12
13	14	15	16	17	18	19
20	21	22	23	24	25	26
27	28	29	30			

OCTOBER
M	T	W	T	F	S	S
				1	2	3
4	5	6	7	8	9	10
11	12	13	14	15	16	17
18	19	20	21	22	23	24
25	26	27	28	29	30	31

NOVEMBER
M	T	W	T	F	S	S
1	2	3	4	5	6	7
8	9	10	11	12	13	14
15	16	17	18	19	20	21
22	23	24	25	26	27	28
29	30					

DECEMBER
M	T	W	T	F	S	S
		1	2	3	4	5
6	7	8	9	10	11	12
13	14	15	16	17	18	19
20	21	22	23	24	25	26
27	28	29	30	31		

CALENDAR 2005

JANUARY
M	T	W	T	F	S	S
					1	2
3	4	5	6	7	8	9
10	11	12	13	14	15	16
17	18	19	20	21	22	23
24	25	26	27	28	29	30
31						

FEBRUARY
M	T	W	T	F	S	S
	1	2	3	4	5	6
7	8	9	10	11	12	13
14	15	16	17	18	19	20
21	22	23	24	25	26	27
28						

MARCH
M	T	W	T	F	S	S
	1	2	3	4	5	6
7	8	9	10	11	12	13
14	15	16	17	18	19	20
21	22	23	24	25	26	27
28	29	30	31			

APRIL
M	T	W	T	F	S	S
				1	2	3
4	5	6	7	8	9	10
11	12	13	14	15	16	17
18	19	20	21	22	23	24
25	26	27	28	29	30	

MAY
M	T	W	T	F	S	S
						1
2	3	4	5	6	7	8
9	10	11	12	13	14	15
16	17	18	19	20	21	22
23	24	25	26	27	28	29
30	31					

JUNE
M	T	W	T	F	S	S
		1	2	3	4	5
6	7	8	9	10	11	12
13	14	15	16	17	18	19
20	21	22	23	24	25	26
27	28	29	30			

JULY
M	T	W	T	F	S	S
				1	2	3
4	5	6	7	8	9	10
11	12	13	14	15	16	17
18	19	20	21	22	23	24
25	26	27	28	29	30	31

AUGUST
M	T	W	T	F	S	S
1	2	3	4	5	6	7
8	9	10	11	12	13	14
15	16	17	18	19	20	21
22	23	24	25	26	27	28
29	30	31				

SEPTEMBER
M	T	W	T	F	S	S
			1	2	3	4
5	6	7	8	9	10	11
12	13	14	15	16	17	18
19	20	21	22	23	24	25
26	27	28	29	30		

OCTOBER
M	T	W	T	F	S	S
					1	2
3	4	5	6	7	8	9
10	11	12	13	14	15	16
17	18	19	20	21	22	23
24	25	26	27	28	29	30
31						

NOVEMBER
M	T	W	T	F	S	S
	1	2	3	4	5	6
7	8	9	10	11	12	13
14	15	16	17	18	19	20
21	22	23	24	25	26	27
28	29	30				

DECEMBER
M	T	W	T	F	S	S
			1	2	3	4
5	6	7	8	9	10	11
12	13	14	15	16	17	18
19	20	21	22	23	24	25
26	27	28	29	30	31	

Introduction

In 1859, on the verge of bankruptcy, the Horticultural Society of London sold its original library. The sale took three days at Sotheby's, thousands of books and drawings were parcelled out in lots, and the total profit to the Society was £1,112 1s. 6d.

Seven years later, when the re-named Royal Horticultural Society was once again flourishing, the private library of its former Secretary, John Lindley, came on the market. Using the profits from the First International Horticultural Exhibition, which it had just helped to stage, the RHS bought Lindley's collection as a partial replacement for the library it had lost. In 1868 the collection was invested in a private trust, the Lindley Library Trust, in order to ensure that it could never again be sold as its predecessor had been. Today, the Lindley Library is a collective term for all the books, periodicals and drawings owned by the Royal Horticultural Society, and occupies five sites, from Harlow Carr in the north to Hyde Hall in the east to Wisley in the south. The largest collection, which also includes the historical collection, is housed in London at 80 Vincent Square.

John Lindley's library comprised some 1,300 volumes. Today, the collection in London alone includes roughly 50,000 volumes, 1,500 periodical titles (about 400 of these are current publications received as gifts or exchanges), trade catalogues from some 7,000 firms worldwide and 28,000 drawings. The collections have been built up by purchase, commission, gifts, exchanges and bequests, and the illustrations in this desk diary have been chosen to show the range of gifts and bequests received by the Lindley Library over the years.

By far the largest single bequest was that of Reginald Cory (1871–1934), a Cardiff coal millionaire who inherited a fine house and garden at the Dyffryn, near Cardiff. Cory lavished his wealth on books and drawings and enthusiastically promoted horticultural causes, from dahlia trials to helping to finance the ailing *Curtis's Botanical Magazine*. His bequest of books and drawings was received in 1936 and returned to the Library some of the very items sold at Sotheby's in 1859.

There have been many other bequests: artists have left their works, owners of celebrated gardens have left collections. Ellen Willmott, whose garden at Warley Place, Essex, is now a country park, left drawings she had commissioned of her irises; E. A. Bowles, whose garden at Myddelton House, Enfield, now belongs to the Lea Valley Water Authority, left a mass of papers, including his own drawings of *Galanthus* and other genera; the archives of garden designers such as Lanning Roper and Michael Haworth-Booth are also deposited. These gifts and bequests are now safeguarded in perpetuity, and the Lindley Library will continue to provide a safe haven for future gifts and bequests, for generations to come.

Brent Elliott
The Royal Horticultural Society

DECEMBER ✧ JANUARY

29 MONDAY

30 TUESDAY

First Quarter

31 WEDNESDAY

New Year's Eve

1 THURSDAY

New Year's Day
Holiday UK, Republic of Ireland, Canada,
USA, Australia and New Zealand

2 FRIDAY

Holiday, Scotland and New Zealand

3 SATURDAY

4 SUNDAY

A drawing of a snowdrop cultivar, *Galanthus* 'Galatea',
by Edward Augustus Bowles. E. A. Bowles bequest, 1954.

JANUARY

MONDAY **5**

TUESDAY **6**

Epiphany

WEDNESDAY **7**

Full Moon

THURSDAY **8**

FRIDAY **9**

SATURDAY **10**

SUNDAY **11**

An early nineteenth-century drawing of the star anemone (*Anemone pavonina*)
by Pierre-Jean-François Turpin, from an album of his drawings on vellum. Reginald Cory bequest, 1936.

JANUARY

12 MONDAY

13 TUESDAY

14 WEDNESDAY

15 THURSDAY

Last Quarter

16 FRIDAY

17 SATURDAY

18 SUNDAY

An early eighteenth-century drawing on vellum of the vanilla orchid (*Vanilla planifolia*)
by Claude Aubriet. Reginald Cory bequest, 1936.

JANUARY

MONDAY **19**

Holiday, USA (Martin Luther King's birthday)

TUESDAY **20**

RHS London Flower Show

WEDNESDAY **21**

New Moon
RHS London Flower Show

THURSDAY **22**

Chinese New Year

FRIDAY **23**

SATURDAY **24**

SUNDAY **25**

A coloured engraving of a bouquet of pansies from *Choix des plus belles fleurs* (1827–33)
by Pierre-Joseph Redouté. Reginald Cory bequest, 1936.

WEEK 4

JANUARY ✧ FEBRUARY

26 MONDAY

Holiday, Australia (Australia Day)

27 TUESDAY

28 WEDNESDAY

29 THURSDAY

First Quarter

30 FRIDAY

31 SATURDAY

1 SUNDAY

WEEK 5

A drawing of *Juniperus communis* from 'Flore du Désert', a collection of plant portraits by an anonymous French artist of the early nineteenth century. Reginald Cory bequest, 1936.

FEBRUARY

MONDAY **2**

TUESDAY **3**

WEDNESDAY **4**

THURSDAY **5**

FRIDAY **6**

Full Moon
Holiday, New Zealand (Waitangi Day)

SATURDAY **7**

SUNDAY **8**

A drawing of species of crocus by Rear-Admiral John Paul Wellington Furse,
observed by him on an expedition to the Near East. Bequest of the artist, 1976.

FEBRUARY

9 MONDAY

10 TUESDAY

11 WEDNESDAY

12 THURSDAY

Holiday, USA (Lincoln's birthday)

13 FRIDAY

Last Quarter

14 SATURDAY

St Valentine's Day

15 SUNDAY

A coloured engraving of *Camellia japonica* from the *Flora Japonica* (1835–70)
of Franz Philipp von Siebold and J. G. Zuccarini. Reginald Cory bequest, 1936.

FEBRUARY

MONDAY **16**

Holiday, USA (Presidents' Day)

TUESDAY **17**

RHS London Flower Show

WEDNESDAY **18**

RHS London Flower Show

THURSDAY **19**

FRIDAY **20**

New Moon

SATURDAY **21**

SUNDAY **22**

Islamic New Year (subject to sighting of the moon)

A late seventeenth-century drawing of a form of *Fritillaria meleagris*
by Pieter van Holsteyn. Reginald Cory bequest, 1936.

FEBRUARY

23 MONDAY

24 TUESDAY

Shrove Tuesday

25 WEDNESDAY

Ash Wednesday

26 THURSDAY

27 FRIDAY

28 SATURDAY

First Quarter

29 SUNDAY

A drawing of the sweet bay (*Laurus nobilis*) from 'Flore du Désert', a collection of plant portraits
by an anonymous French artist of the early nineteenth century. Reginald Cory bequest, 1936.

MARCH

MONDAY **1**

St David's Day

TUESDAY **2**

WEDNESDAY **3**

THURSDAY **4**

FRIDAY **5**

SATURDAY **6**

Full Moon

SUNDAY **7**

A drawing of the poppy anemone (*Anemone coronaria* var. *phoenicia*)
by Edward Augustus Bowles. E.A. Bowles bequest, 1954.

WEEK 10

MARCH

8 MONDAY

Commonwealth Day

9 TUESDAY

RHS London Flower Show

10 WEDNESDAY

RHS London Flower Show

11 THURSDAY

12 FRIDAY

13 SATURDAY

Last Quarter
RHS London Orchid Show

14 SUNDAY

RHS London Orchid Show

A drawing of *Callistemon citrina*
by Winifred Baker. Gertrude Baker bequest, 1955.

MONDAY **15**

TUESDAY **16**

WEDNESDAY **17**

St Patrick's Day
Holiday, Northern Ireland and Republic of Ireland

THURSDAY **18**

FRIDAY **19**

SATURDAY **20**

New Moon
Vernal Equinox

SUNDAY **21**

Mothering Sunday, UK

A coloured stipple engraving of *Magnolia × soulangiana* from *Choix des plus belles fleurs* (1827–33)
by Pierre-Joseph Redouté. Reginald Cory bequest, 1936.

MARCH

22 MONDAY

23 TUESDAY

24 WEDNESDAY

25 THURSDAY

26 FRIDAY

27 SATURDAY

28 SUNDAY

First Quarter
British Summer Time begins

A drawing of daffodil 'Dawn', dated 1913,
by Edward Augustus Bowles. E. A. Bowles bequest, 1954.

MONDAY **29**

TUESDAY **30**

WEDNESDAY **31**

THURSDAY **1**

FRIDAY **2**

SATURDAY **3**

SUNDAY **4**

Palm Sunday

A late eighteenth-century drawing of *Hiptage madablota*, from 'Flora Asiatica', a collection of drawings
by anonymous artists formerly in the collection of the 3rd Earl of Bute. Reginald Cory bequest, 1936.

APRIL

5 MONDAY

Full Moon

6 TUESDAY

Passover (Pesach), First Day
RHS London Flower Show

7 WEDNESDAY

RHS London Flower Show

8 THURSDAY

Maundy Thursday

9 FRIDAY

Good Friday
Holiday, UK, Republic of Ireland, Canada
USA, Australia and New Zealand

10 SATURDAY

11 SUNDAY

Easter Sunday

A drawing of *Prunus hirtipes* 'Semi-plena'
by Winifred Baker. Gertrude Baker bequest, 1955.

APRIL

Last Quarter
Easter Monday
Holiday, UK (exc. Scotland), Republic of Ireland,
Canada, USA, Australia and New Zealand
Passover (Pesach), Seventh Day

TUESDAY **13**

Passover (Pesach), Eighth Day

WEDNESDAY **14**

THURSDAY **15**

FRIDAY **16**

SATURDAY **17**

RHS Plant Roadshow, Torquay (to be confirmed)

SUNDAY **18**

RHS Plant Roadshow, Torquay (to be confirmed)

An early eighteenth-century drawing of tulip 'Prins d'Orange Blanc', attributed to August Sievert
(but in 1775 reproduced in C. J. Trew's *Hortus Nitidissimis* as tulip 'Keizer Leopoldus'). Reginald Cory bequest, 1936.   WEEK 16

APRIL

19 MONDAY

New Moon

20 TUESDAY

21 WEDNESDAY

Birthday of Queen Elizabeth II

22 THURSDAY

23 FRIDAY

St George's Day

24 SATURDAY

25 SUNDAY

A drawing of the horse chestnut (*Aesculus* × *carnea*)
by Winifred Baker. Gertrude Baker bequest, 1955.

MONDAY **26**

Holiday, Australia and New Zealand (Anzac Day)

TUESDAY **27**

First Quarter
RHS London Flower Show (to be confirmed)

WEDNESDAY **28**

RHS London Flower Show (to be confirmed)

THURSDAY **29**

FRIDAY **30**

SATURDAY **1**

SUNDAY **2**

An early eighteenth-century drawing of tulip 'Prins Frederick',
attributed to August Sievert. This drawing served as the basis for plate 31 in the
first volume of C. J. Trew's *Hortus Nitidissimis* (1750–68). Reginald Cory bequest, 1936.

MAY

3 MONDAY

Early May Bank Holiday, UK
and Republic of Ireland

4 TUESDAY

Full Moon

5 WEDNESDAY

6 THURSDAY

7 FRIDAY

Malvern Spring Gardening Show

8 SATURDAY

Malvern Spring Gardening Show

9 SUNDAY

Mother's Day, Canada, USA,
Australia and New Zealand
Malvern Spring Gardening Show

A drawing of *Iris germanica* from 'Flore du Désert', a collection of plant portraits
by an anonymous French artist of the early nineteenth century. Reginald Cory bequest, 1936.

WEEK 19

MAY

MONDAY **10**

TUESDAY **11**

Last Quarter

WEDNESDAY **12**

THURSDAY **13**

FRIDAY **14**

SATURDAY **15**

SUNDAY **16**

A drawing of *Tulipa gesneriana* from 'Flore du Désert', a collection of plant portraits
by an anonymous French artist of the early nineteenth century. Reginald Cory bequest, 1936.

MAY

17 MONDAY

18 TUESDAY

19 WEDNESDAY

New Moon

20 THURSDAY

Ascension Day

21 FRIDAY

22 SATURDAY

23 SUNDAY

A drawing of *Wisteria sinensis* (probably 1920s)
by Ruth Collingridge. Reginald Cory bequest, 1936.

MONDAY **24**

Holiday, Canada (Victoria Day)

TUESDAY **25**

Chelsea Flower Show

WEDNESDAY **26**

Jewish Feast of Weeks (Shavuot)
Chelsea Flower Show

THURSDAY **27**

First Quarter
Chelsea Flower Show

FRIDAY **28**

Chelsea Flower Show

SATURDAY **29**

SUNDAY **30**

Whit Sunday (Pentecost)

A late nineteenth-century drawing of the oriental poppy (*Papaver orientale*)
by Ruth Glaister. Gift of Mrs Agnes Elmhurst, 1954.

MAY ✧ JUNE

31 MONDAY

1 TUESDAY

2 WEDNESDAY

3 THURSDAY

Full Moon

4 FRIDAY

5 SATURDAY

6 SUNDAY

Trinity Sunday

WEEK 23

A late nineteenth-century drawing of *Clematis × jackmanii*
by Ruth Glaister. Gift of Mrs Agnes Elmhurst, 1954.

JUNE

MONDAY **7**

Holiday, New Zealand (The Queen's birthday)

TUESDAY **8**

WEDNESDAY **9**

Last Quarter

THURSDAY **10**

Corpus Christi

FRIDAY **11**

SATURDAY **12**

The Queen's official birthday
(subject to confirmaton)

SUNDAY **13**

A drawing of *Rosa foetida* 'Bicolor',
by Emma or Emmeline Smith (*fl.* 1780s). Reginald Cory bequest, 1936.

WEEK 24

JUNE

14 MONDAY

Holiday, Australia (The Queen's birthday)

15 TUESDAY

16 WEDNESDAY

BBC Gardeners' World Live, Birmingham

17 THURSDAY

New Moon
BBC Gardeners' World Live, Birmingham

18 FRIDAY

BBC Gardeners' World Live, Birmingham

19 SATURDAY

BBC Gardeners' World Live, Birmingham

20 SUNDAY

Father's Day, UK, Canada and USA
BBC Gardeners' World Live, Birmingham

WEEK 25

A late seventeenth-century drawing of cherry cultivars,
by Pieter van Holsteyn. Reginald Cory bequest, 1936.

JUNE

MONDAY 21

Summer Solstice

TUESDAY 22

First Wisley Flower Show

WEDNESDAY 23

First Wisley Flower Show

THURSDAY 24

First Wisley Flower Show

FRIDAY 25

First Quarter

SATURDAY 26

SUNDAY 27

A drawing of an iris of the Monspur group, by a Miss Williamson,
made in 1905 for Ellen Willmott of Warley Place, Essex. Ellen Willmott bequest, 1935.

JUNE ✧ JULY

28 MONDAY

29 TUESDAY

30 WEDNESDAY

1 THURSDAY

Holiday, Canada (Canada Day)
RHS London Flower Show

2 FRIDAY

Full Moon
RHS London Flower Show

3 SATURDAY

RHS London Flower Show

4 SUNDAY

Independence Day, USA

A drawing of *Iris cuprea* (now *Iris fulva*) by a Miss Williamson,
made in 1905 for Ellen Willmott of Warley Place, Essex. Ellen Willmott bequest, 1935.

JULY

MONDAY **5**

Holiday, USA (Independence Day)

TUESDAY **6**

Hampton Court Palace Flower Show

WEDNESDAY **7**

Hampton Court Palace Flower Show

THURSDAY **8**

Hampton Court Palace Flower Show

FRIDAY **9**

Last Quarter
Hampton Court Palace Flower Show

SATURDAY **10**

Hampton Court Palace Flower Show

SUNDAY **11**

Hampton Court Palace Flower Show

A drawing of *Rosa* 'Rubrotincta' by Alfred Parsons: an original drawing
for Ellen Willmott's *Genus Rosa* (1910–14). Reginald Cory bequest, 1936.

JULY

12 MONDAY

Holiday, Northern Ireland (Battle of the Boyne)

13 TUESDAY

14 WEDNESDAY

15 THURSDAY

St Swithin's Day

16 FRIDAY

17 SATURDAY

New Moon

18 SUNDAY

WEEK 29

A drawing of roses, dated 1755,
by Michiel van Huysum. Reginald Cory bequest, 1936.

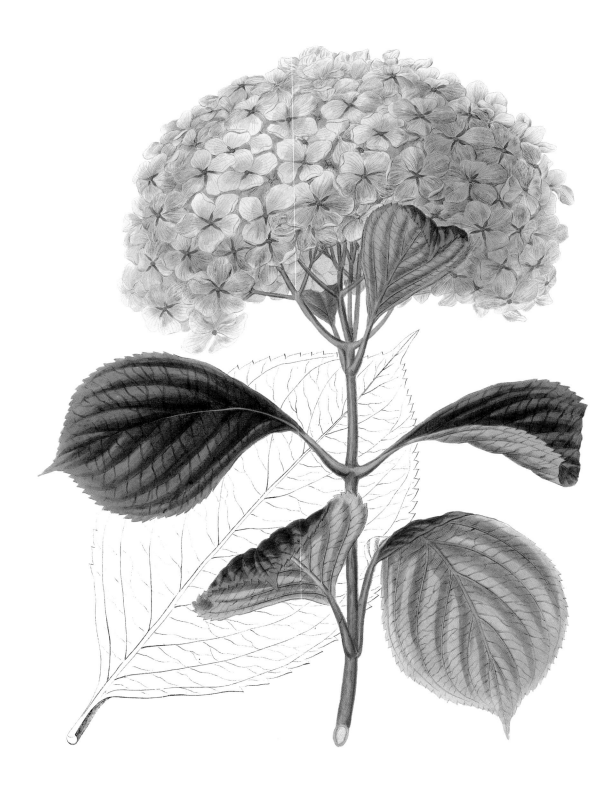

JULY

MONDAY **19**

TUESDAY **20**

WEDNESDAY **21**

The RHS Flower Show at Tatton Park

THURSDAY **22**

The RHS Flower Show at Tatton Park

FRIDAY **23**

The RHS Flower Show at Tatton Park

SATURDAY **24**

The RHS Flower Show at Tatton Park

SUNDAY **25**

First Quarter
The RHS Flower Show at Tatton Park

A coloured engraving of *Hydrangea macrophylla* 'Otaksa' from the *Flora Japonica* (1835–70)
of Franz Philipp von Siebold and J. G. Zuccarini. Reginald Cory bequest, 1936.

JULY ✧ AUGUST

26 MONDAY

27 TUESDAY

28 WEDNESDAY

29 THURSDAY

30 FRIDAY

31 SATURDAY

Full Moon

1 SUNDAY

A drawing of an aconite (probably 1820s)
by James Sowerby. E. A. Bowles bequest, 1954.

AUGUST

MONDAY **2**

Summer Bank Holiday, Scotland
and Republic of Ireland

TUESDAY **3**

WEDNESDAY **4**

THURSDAY **5**

FRIDAY **6**

SATURDAY **7**

Last Quarter

SUNDAY **8**

A coloured engraving of a sunflower (*Helianthus annuus*)
from *Illustration of the Sexual System of Linnaeus* (1770–77)
by John Miller (Johann Sebastian Müller). Reginald Cory bequest, 1936.

WEEK 32

AUGUST

9 MONDAY

10 TUESDAY

11 WEDNESDAY

12 THURSDAY

13 FRIDAY

14 SATURDAY

15 SUNDAY

A late eighteenth-century drawing of the common myrtle (*Myrtus communis*) from 'Flora Asiatica', a collection of drawings by anonymous artists formerly in the collection of the 3rd Earl of Bute. Reginald Cory bequest, 1936.

AUGUST

MONDAY **16**

New Moon

TUESDAY **17**

Second Wisley Flower Show

WEDNESDAY **18**

Second Wisley Flower Show

THURSDAY **19**

Second Wisley Flower Show

FRIDAY **20**

SATURDAY **21**

SUNDAY **22**

A coloured engraving after J. Hart of *Helianthemum canescens* (later renamed *H. variabile*), from *Cistineae* (1825–30) by Robert Sweet. Reginald Cory bequest, 1936.

WEEK 34

AUGUST

23 MONDAY

First Quarter

24 TUESDAY

25 WEDNESDAY

26 THURSDAY

27 FRIDAY

28 SATURDAY

29 SUNDAY

A late seventeenth-century drawing of an acanthus
by Pieter van Holsteyn. Reginald Cory bequest, 1936.

MONDAY 30

Full Moon
Summer Bank Holiday, UK (exc. Scotland)

TUESDAY 31

WEDNESDAY 1

THURSDAY 2

FRIDAY 3

SATURDAY 4

SUNDAY 5

Father's Day, Australia and New Zealand

A drawing of the blackberry (*Rubus fruticosus*) dated 1784,
by Margaret Meen. Reginald Cory bequest, 1936.

SEPTEMBER

6 MONDAY

Last Quarter
Holiday, Canada (Labour Day) and USA (Labor Day)

7 TUESDAY

8 WEDNESDAY

9 THURSDAY

10 FRIDAY

11 SATURDAY

12 SUNDAY

A drawing of *Tropaeolum majus* from 'Flore du Désert', a collection of plant portraits
by an anonymous French artist of the early nineteenth century. Reginald Cory bequest, 1936.

SEPTEMBER

MONDAY **13**

TUESDAY **14**

New Moon
RHS Great Autumn Show, London

WEDNESDAY **15**

RHS Great Autumn Show, London

THURSDAY **16**

Jewish New Year (Rosh Hashanah)

FRIDAY **17**

SATURDAY **18**

SUNDAY **19**

A coloured engraving of a fig cultivar, 'Fico rubado',
from the *Pomona italiana* (1817–39) of Giorgio Gallesio. Reginald Cory bequest, 1936

SEPTEMBER

---

20 MONDAY

---

21 TUESDAY

First Quarter

22 WEDNESDAY

Autumnal Equinox

23 THURSDAY

---

24 FRIDAY

---

25 SATURDAY

Jewish Day of Atonement (Yom Kippur)
Malvern Autumn Garden and Country Show

26 SUNDAY

Malvern Autumn Garden and Country Show

WEEK 39

A drawing of rudbeckia (probably 1820s)
by James Sowerby. E. A. Bowles bequest, 1954.

MONDAY **27**

TUESDAY **28**

Full Moon

WEDNESDAY **29**

Michaelmas Day

THURSDAY **30**

Jewish Festival of Tabernacles (Succoth), First Day

FRIDAY **1**

SATURDAY **2**

SUNDAY **3**

A drawing of *Abutilon megapotanicum*
by Winifred Baker. Gertrude Baker bequest, 1955.

OCTOBER

4 MONDAY

5 TUESDAY

RHS London Flower Show

6 WEDNESDAY

Last Quarter
RHS London Flower Show

7 THURSDAY

Jewish Festival of Tabernacles (Succoth), Eighth Day

8 FRIDAY

9 SATURDAY

10 SUNDAY

A drawing of *Campsis radicans*, dated 1785,
by Margaret Meen. Reginald Cory bequest, 1936.

OCTOBER

MONDAY 11

Holiday, Canada (Thanksgiving Day)
Holiday, USA (Columbus Day)

TUESDAY 12

WEDNESDAY 13

THURSDAY 14

New Moon

FRIDAY 15

First Day of Ramadân
(subject to sighting of the moon)

SATURDAY 16

SUNDAY 17

A drawing of *Passiflora laurifolia*, dated 1785,
by Margaret Meen. Reginald Cory bequest, 1936.

OCTOBER

18 MONDAY

19 TUESDAY

20 WEDNESDAY

First Quarter

21 THURSDAY

22 FRIDAY

23 SATURDAY

24 SUNDAY

United Nations Day

WEEK 43

A drawing of *Amaranthus tricolor* (probably 1780s)
by Margaret Meen. Reginald Cory bequest, 1936.

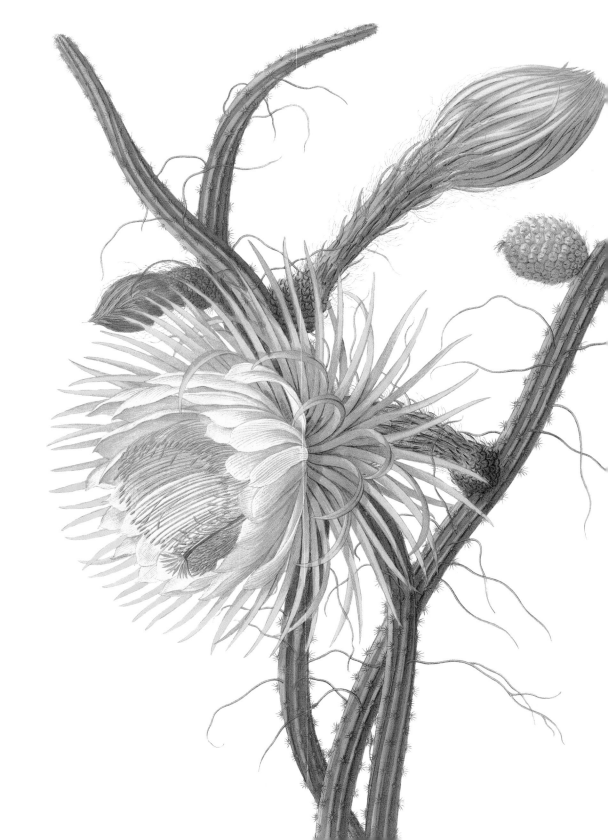

OCTOBER

MONDAY **25**

Holiday, Republic of Ireland
Holiday, New Zealand (Labour Day)

TUESDAY **26**

WEDNESDAY **27**

THURSDAY **28**

Full Moon

FRIDAY **29**

SATURDAY **30**

SUNDAY **31**

Hallowe'en
British Summer Time ends

A coloured engraving after Georg Dionysius Ehret of a night-blooming cereus (*Selenicereus grandiflora*)
from C. J. Trew's *Plantae Selectae* (1750–65). Reginald Cory bequest, 1936.

WEEK 44

NOVEMBER

1 MONDAY

All Saints' Day

2 TUESDAY

3 WEDNESDAY

4 THURSDAY

5 FRIDAY

Last Quarter
Guy Fawkes' Day

6 SATURDAY

7 SUNDAY

A coloured engraving of *Crinum asiaticum* var. *sinicum* from *A Selection of Hexandrian Plants* (1831–4) by Mrs Edward Bury (née Priscilla Susan Falkner). Reginald Cory bequest, 1936.

NOVEMBER

MONDAY **8**

TUESDAY **9**

WEDNESDAY **10**

THURSDAY **11**

Holiday, Canada (Remembrance Day)
Holiday, USA (Veterans' Day)

FRIDAY **12**

New Moon

SATURDAY **13**

SUNDAY **14**

Remembrance Sunday, UK

A drawing of the grape cultivar 'Chasselas verd' by Johann Simon Kerner,
from his *Le Raisin* (1803–8). Kerner produced *Le Raisin* as one of his limited-edition works,
in which all the illustrations were drawn individually rather than printed. Reginald Cory bequest, 1936.

WEEK 46

NOVEMBER

15 MONDAY

16 TUESDAY

17 WEDNESDAY

18 THURSDAY

19 FRIDAY

First Quarter

20 SATURDAY

21 SUNDAY

A drawing of the hawthorn (*Crataegus monogyna*), probably 1780s,
by Augusta Smith. Reginald Cory bequest, 1936.

NOVEMBER

MONDAY **22**

TUESDAY **23**

RHS London Flower Show

WEDNESDAY **24**

RHS London Flower Show

THURSDAY **25**

Holiday, USA (Thanksgiving Day)

FRIDAY **26**

Full Moon

SATURDAY **27**

SUNDAY **28**

Advent Sunday

An eighteenth-century drawing of fungi, attributed to Thomas Robins the Elder, from an album formerly belonging to the Duchess of Cavendish. Reginald Cory bequest, 1936.

WEEK 48

NOVEMBER ✧ DECEMBER

29 MONDAY

30 TUESDAY

St Andrew's Day

1 WEDNESDAY

2 THURSDAY

3 FRIDAY

4 SATURDAY

5 SUNDAY

Last Quarter

A drawing of the Turkey oak (*Quercus cerris*), probably 1780s, by Margaret Meen. Reginald Cory bequest, 1936.

DECEMBER

MONDAY **6**

TUESDAY **7**

WEDNESDAY **8**

Jewish Festival of Chanukah, First Day

THURSDAY **9**

FRIDAY **10**

SATURDAY **11**

SUNDAY **12**

New Moon

A coloured engraving of *Amaryllis pulverulenta* (now *Hippeastrum striatum*)
from *A Selection of Hexandrian Plants* (1831–4) by Mrs Edward Bury
(née Priscilla Susan Falkner). Reginald Cory bequest, 1936.

DECEMBER

13 MONDAY

14 TUESDAY

15 WEDNESDAY

16 THURSDAY

17 FRIDAY

18 SATURDAY

First Quarter

19 SUNDAY

A drawing of common holly (*Ilex aquifolium*)
by Dorothy Martin. Bequest of the artist, 1950.

DECEMBER

MONDAY **20**

TUESDAY **21**

Winter Solstice

WEDNESDAY **22**

THURSDAY **23**

FRIDAY **24**

Christmas Eve
Holiday, USA (Christmas Day observed)

SATURDAY **25**

Christmas Day

SUNDAY **26**

Full Moon
Boxing Day (St Stephen's Day)

An early nineteenth-century drawing of a hellebore by Pierre-Jean-François Turpin,
from an album of his drawings on vellum. Reginald Cory bequest, 1936.

WEEK 52

DECEMBER ✧ JANUARY

27 MONDAY

Holiday, UK, Republic of Ireland,
Canada, Australia and New Zealand

28 TUESDAY

Holiday, UK, Republic of Ireland,
Canada, Australia and New Zealand

29 WEDNESDAY

30 THURSDAY

31 FRIDAY

New Year's Eve
Holiday, USA (New Year's Day observed)

1 SATURDAY

New Year's Day

2 SUNDAY

WEEK 53

A drawing of the Colorado spruce (*Picea pungens glauca*)
by Ursula Hodgson. Gift of the artist, 1987.

European National Holidays 2004

AUSTRIA Jan. 1, 6; April 11, 12; May 1, 20, 30, 31; June 10; Aug. 15; Oct. 26; Nov. 1; Dec. 8, 25, 26

BELGIUM Jan. 1; April 11, 12; May 1, 20, 30, 31; July 21; Aug. 15; Nov. 1, 2, 11; Dec. 25

DENMARK Jan. 1; April 8, 9, 11, 12; May 7, 20, 30, 31; June 5; Dec. 25, 26

FINLAND Jan. 1, 6; April 9, 11, 12; May 1, 20, 30; June 26; Nov. 6; Dec. 6, 25, 26

FRANCE Jan. 1; April 11, 12; May 1, 8, 20, 30, 31; July 14; Aug. 15; Nov. 1, 11; Dec. 25

GERMANY Jan. 1, 6; April 9, 11, 12; May 1, 20, 30, 31; June 10; Aug. 15; Oct. 3, 31; Nov. 1, 17; Dec. 25, 26

GREECE Jan. 1, 6; Feb. 23; March 25; April 9, 11, 12; May 1, 30, 31; Aug. 15; Oct. 28; Dec. 25, 26

ITALY Jan. 1, 6; April 11, 12, 25; May 1; Aug. 15; Nov. 1; Dec. 8, 25, 26

LUXEMBOURG Jan. 1; Feb. 23; April 11, 12; May 1, 20, 30, 31; June 23; Aug. 15; Nov. 1, 2; Dec. 25, 26

NETHERLANDS Jan. 1; April 9, 11, 12, 30; May 5, 20, 30, 31; Dec. 25, 26

NORWAY Jan. 1; April 8, 9, 11, 12; May 1, 17, 20, 30, 31; Dec. 25, 26

PORTUGAL Jan. 1; Feb. 24; April 9, 11, 25; May 1; June 10; Aug. 15; Oct. 5; Nov. 1; Dec. 1, 8, 25

SPAIN Jan. 1, 6; March 19; April 8, 9, 11, 12; May 1, 30; July 25; Aug. 15; Oct. 12; Nov. 1; Dec. 6, 8, 25, 26

SWEDEN Jan. 1, 6; April 9, 11, 12; May 1, 20, 30, 31; June 26; Nov. 6; Dec. 25, 26

SWITZERLAND Jan. 1; April 9, 11, 12; May 1, 20, 30, 31; Aug. 1; Nov. 1; Dec. 25, 26